Where is Pig?

by Rob Arego

illustrated by Tim Bowers

Harcourt

Orlando   Boston   Dallas   Chicago   San Diego

www.harcourtschool.com

Cat is on the beach.

Where is Pig?

Ram is on the beach.

Where is Pig?

Bat is on the beach.

Where is Pig?

Pig is on the beach.